HEINEMANN MATHEMATICS 5

Reinforcement Sheets

Heinemann Mathematics 5 is intended for children
• working at Level 4 of the National Curriculum (England and Wales) and Common Curriculum (Northern Ireland)
• working at Level C and moving into Level D of Mathematics 5–14 (Scotland)

Heinemann

Heinemann Educational Publishing
Halley Court, Jordan Hill, Oxford OX2 8EJ
a division of Reed Educational & Professional Publishing Ltd

MELBOURNE AUCKLAND
FLORENCE PRAGUE MADRID ATHENS
SINGAPORE TOKYO SAO PAULO
CHICAGO PORTSMOUTH (NH) MEXICO
IBADAN GABARONE JOHANNESBURG
KAMPALA NAIROBI

ISBN 0 435 021982

First published 1994
96 97 98 99   10 9 8 7 6

Writing Team

John T Blair
Ian K Clark
Aileen P Duncan
Percy W Farren
Archie MacCallum
John Mackinlay
Myra A Pearson
Catherine D J Preston
Dorothy S Simpson
John W Thayers
David K Thomson

Designed and produced by Oxprint Ltd
Printed in the UK by Athenaeum Press Ltd, Gateshead, Tyne & Wear.

Introduction

- This booklet contains 30 photocopiable reinforcement sheets designed to provide further practice in selected topics for children using Heinemann Mathematics 5.

- Each sheet is referenced from a specific page of the Heinemann Mathematics 5 Textbook or Workbook and is designed to supplement the mathematics of the section from which it is referenced.

  For example, page 22 of the Textbook carries the symbol

  $$\boxed{\text{R}7}$$

  to indicate that reinforcement sheet 7 is available to provide further practice in the aspect dealt with in that section, ie multiplication of HTU by 2 to 10. Conversely, the top right-hand corner of each reinforcement sheet states the core page from which it is referenced.

- A list of the sheets, with the mathematical topics they cover and references to Textbook and Workbook pages, is given on the next page.
  References to Attainment Targets are not provided in this booklet. The appropriate targets are those of the core pages to which the sheets are linked and can be found in the Teacher's Notes.

- The Teacher's Notes list reinforcement sheets in the Overview section for each mathematical topic. The 'R' symbol described above also appears beside the notes for any core page which has an associated reinforcement sheet.

- There are no teaching notes for reinforcement sheets. Their content is similar to that of their associated core pages, for which introductory activities appear in the Teacher's Notes.

- Each sheet is intended to be used *selectively* with those children who show a need for some extra practice over and above that provided in the core materials.
  There is no advantage in using the sheets routinely with children who have already mastered the work. They would be better engaged in using the Extension Textbook, the Problem Solving Activities in the Assessment and Resources Pack, or in tackling a new topic.
  The sheets are not designed to assist those pupils whose understanding of the topic is so poor that they really require further teaching before engaging in more practice.

- In most cases the reinforcement sheets continue the *context* of the core section to which they relate. This is intended to make it easier to integrate them with on-going work when supplementary examples are required for some children.

- Some of the sheets have a fill-in format. A 'pencil' symbol appears beside the number of the sheet in these cases. $\boxed{18\mathcal{O}}$

- The only materials required are calculators and coloured pencils. An analogue clock may be helpful to some pupils.

- Answers for the Reinforcement Sheets are provided at the end of this booklet.

Mathematical content

Reinforcement sheet		Topic	Referenced from
1	In Emerald Forest	Numbers to 9999: place value	Workbook page 3
2	More tree puzzles	Numbers to 9999: place value	Textbook page 8
3	Trogball	Addition of ThHTU	Textbook page 10
4	Trog holiday survey	Subtraction of ThHTU	Textbook page 12
5	Trogs in the swim	Addition and subtraction of ThHTU	Textbook page 12
6	The four explorers	Money to £20	Textbook page 16
7	Comic collectors	Multiplication: HTU by 2 to 10	Textbook page 22
8	Gifts	Multiplication: HTU by 2 to 10	Textbook page 22
9	*Speedprint*	Multiplication: ThHTU by 2 to 9	Workbook page 6
10	Subscriptions	Multiplication: ThHTU by 2 to 9, money	Textbook page 25
11	*School Scene* competition	+, − of HTU: estimation	Textbook page 30
12	Carnival café	Division: HTU by 2, 3, 4, 5	Textbook page 36
13	Dragons	Division: TU and HTU by 6 and 7	Textbook page 38
14	Street decorations	Division: TU and HTU by 8 and 9	Textbook page 40
15	Carnival events	Division: consolidation	Textbook page 42
16	Carnival fireworks	Division: using a calculator	Textbook page 43
17	Carnival flags	Fractions: $\frac{1}{6}, \frac{1}{7}, \frac{1}{8}, \frac{1}{9}$, link with division	Textbook page 45
18	More carnival flags	Fractions: equivalence	Workbook page 12
19	Pennant parade	Decimals: notation	Workbook page 13
20	Hot air	Decimals: units and tenths	Textbook page 53
21	Boat lengths	Decimals: addition and subtraction	Textbook page 56
22	*Keep Dry Clothing*	Decimals: multiplication	Textbook page 58
23	Orders	Decimals: division	Textbook page 60
24	Sailing club	Multiplication: distributive law, TU by multiples of 10	Textbook page 62
25	Training	Length: m and cm, +, −	Textbook page 70
26	Lotions and potions	Weight: reading scales	Textbook page 78
27	Kluless Cleaner	Weight: scales	Workbook page 29
28	Sports day	Time: durations	Textbook page 86
29	Laser World	Time: durations; counting on, counting back	Textbook page 88
30	Sandra's yacht	Angles: degrees and directions	Textbook page 104

In Emerald Forest

1 Complete:

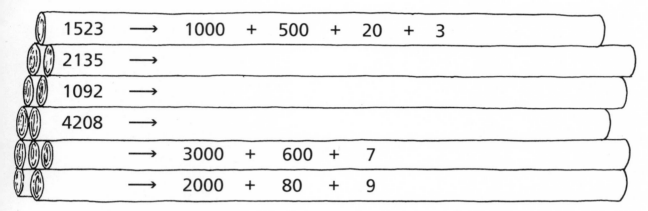

1523 ⟶ 1000 + 500 + 20 + 3

2135 ⟶

1092 ⟶

4208 ⟶

⟶ 3000 + 600 + 7

⟶ 2000 + 80 + 9

2 Write the values of each circled digit.

1 7 ④ 2   3 ④ 1 6   ④ 7 1 2   6 2 1 ⑤

____ 4 tens ____   _____   _____   _____

3 Complete:

17 hundreds = ____ thousand + ____ hundreds = __1700__

24 hundreds = ____ thousands + ____ hundreds = _____

30 hundreds = ____ thousands + ____ hundreds = _____

4 Write these numbers in words:

1702 m _____

1030 m _____

5 For each toadstool write • the number before
• the number after.

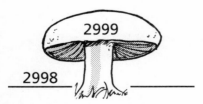

2999

2998 _____

6000

_____

5050

_____

© SPMG 1994. Restricted copyright cleared.

Heinemann Mathematics 5

More tree puzzles

1 Copy and complete each sequence.

(a) 1200, 1400, 1600, _____ , _____ , _____

(b) 1300, 1200, 1100, _____ , _____ , _____

(c) 2060, 2070, 2080, _____ , _____ , _____

(d) 3000, 2500, 2000, _____ , _____ , _____

2 Write these as numbers.

(a) two thousand two hundred

(b) one thousand, two hundred and six

(c) two thousand and sixty

(d) one thousand and eight

3 Write each set of numbers in order, starting with the smallest.

(a) 5090 4809 4076 4300 5190

(b) 1100 1101 1111 1110 1001

4 Use all four digits each time.
Write **(a)** the largest number
   (b) the second largest number
   (c) the second smallest number.

2 2
3 3

5 Add one number each time. Write the number you added.

(a) 3405. → 3505.   (b) 2071. → 4071.   (c) 2551. → 2591.

6 Subtract one number each time. Write the number you subtracted.

(a) 5182. → 5132.   (b) 3500. → 500.   (c) 2355. → 2155.

Trogball

The Millitrogs are having
a trogball match.

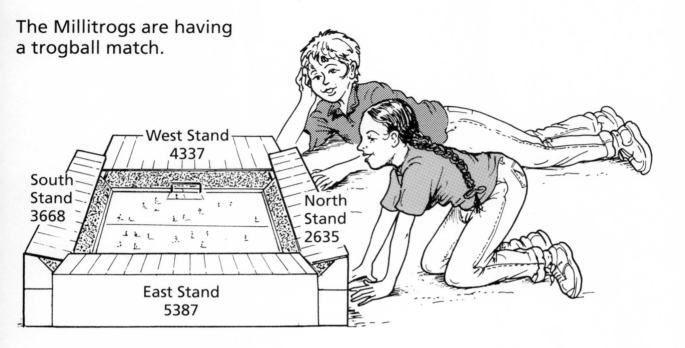

West Stand
4337

South
Stand
3668

North
Stand
2635

East Stand
5387

1 Find the total number of Millitrogs in these stands:
   (a) North and West **(b)** West and East **(c)** South and East
   (d) North and East **(e)** South and West **(f)** North and South.

2 Find the total number sold:
   (a) hats and mugs
   (b) hats and flags
   (c) ties and flags
   (d) ties and hats
   (e) mugs and ties
   (f) mugs and flags.

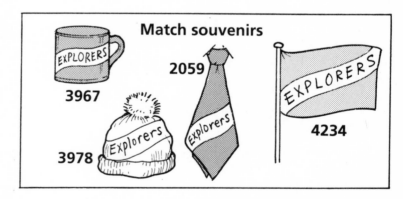

Match souvenirs

3967   2059   4234   3978

3 The Millitrogs sew together scarves to make a flag for each explorer.
   The table shows the number of each colour of scarf used.

	red	yellow	pink	white
Kelvin	4392	605	9	25
Tony	483	2485	32	1
Lisa	7	263	1045	2112
Kate	300	82	5203	643

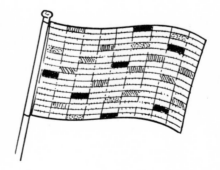

How many scarves were sewn together for
   (a) Kelvin **(b)** Tony **(c)** Lisa **(d)** Kate?

Trog holiday survey

Kelvin's survey shows where the
Millitrogs would like to go on holiday.

Golden Pond	7562	Gem Leaf	2579
Pearl Garden	3249	Ruby River	1776
Emerald Forest	2804		

1 Find the difference between the number who chose
Golden Pond and the number who chose

  (a) Pearl Garden   **(b)** Emerald Forest

  (c) Gem Leaf   **(d)** Ruby River.

2 How many more Millitrogs chose Emerald Forest than chose Ruby River?

3 Some Millitrogs go to Golden
Pond for a holiday cruise.
How many **fewer** Millitrogs are on

  (a) *Bess* than on *Queen*

  (b) *Grace* than on *Lite*

  (c) *Rust* than on *Patch*?

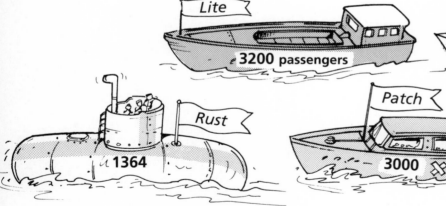

4 The shop at Golden Pond keeps a record of the sun creams sold.
How many more bottles were sold of

  (a) Tan-easy than Protect

  (b) Slotan than Protect

  (c) Smoothglo than Tan-easy

  (d) Smoothglo than Protect?

Tan-easy	3574
Protect	1685
Slotan	5503
Smoothglo	4000

Trogs in the swim

Before they leave, the Explorers help the Millitrogs to build a swimming pool.

1 Find the number of sacks of each left.

(a)	**fine sand**	(b)	**coarse sand**	(c)	**cement**
start	3642	start	3307	start	6005
used	−1644	used	−2639	used	−2347

2 Find the total number of each colour of brick used.

(a) red: 5643 and 3257 (b) yellow: 3526 and 4675

(c) grey: 2839 and 6704 (d) pink: 3547 and 4684

3 (a) How many more red tiles than grey tiles were used?

(b) How many **fewer** yellow tiles than red tiles were used?

Tiles used

Red	3002
Grey	1564
Yellow	2173

4 (a) How many plumbers and plasterers were there altogether?

(b) How many more plasterers than plumbers were there?

(c) How many **fewer** plasterers than brick-layers were there?

Trogs

Plumbers	1637
Plasterers	2495
Brick-layers	3400

5 The Millitrogs made 6000 slabs. When the pool was finished they had 1467 left. How many had they used?

6 On the Opening Day,

(a) how many Millitrogs used the pool?

(b) how many more Millitrogs used the pool in the afternoon than in the morning?

Trog News

OPENING DAY CELEBRATIONS

Our records show attendances of:

4185 Millitrogs in the morning
5020 Millitrogs in the afternoon

Everyone enjoyed the day's events.
A special thanks must be

The four explorers

The four explorers use these prices to plan a trip to
Castle Shopping Mall.

Transport	
Train	£3·76
Bus	£1·89

Food	
Snack	£2·75
Meal	£4·89

Entertainment	
Pictures	£4·80
Ice-rink	£6·20

1 How much will it cost for one person to
   (a) go by train, have a snack and go the pictures?
   (b) go by bus, have a meal and go to the ice rink?

2 How much more does it cost to go by train than by bus?

3 What is the difference in price between a meal and a snack?

4 List the notes and coins Lisa could get in change from £10 if she
   (a) went to the ice-rink   **(b)** bought a train ticket.

5 Kelvin has £10. How much would he have left if he went by bus and then
   to the pictures?

Each explorer has £10 to spend.

6 **(a)** Could Kate go by train and go to the ice rink?
   (b) Could Kate go by train, have a snack and go to the pictures?

7 How much more would Tony need to go by train, have a meal
   and go to the ice rink?

8 Is it possible for Kelvin to go to Castle Shopping Mall, eat and
   then go to an entertainment? Explain your answer.

Comic collectors

Some children in Class 5 collect comics.

I have 3 bundles each with 231 comics.

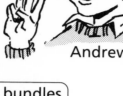

Andrew

Sarah

I have 5 bundles each with 182 comics.

I have 4 bundles each with 307 comics.

Humera

I have 2 bundles each with 236 comics.

Asif

1 How many comics does each child have?

2 Jim has 143 issues of *Laugh-in!* How many pages altogether does he have of
- (a) jokes
- (b) competitions
- (c) letters
- (d) cartoons?

Laugh-in!

IN EVERY ISSUE
4 pages of jokes
2 pages of competitions
3 pages of letters
8 pages of cartoons

3 (a) John has 258 issues of *Pop-Life*. How many pages of songs does he have?

(b) Vicky has 167 issues of *Tina*. How many stories does she have?

POP-LIFE

Each issue has 3 pages of new songs.

Tina

9 stories in every issue.

4 Debbie looks at the comic stall at a jumble sale.
How many comics are there about
- (a) *Sport* – 6 bundles of 145?
- (b) *Pop* – 7 bundles of 249?
- (c) *Animals* – 10 bundles of 350?

Gifts

1 Six joke cards are given free in this week's *Laugh-in!* How many joke cards are in

   (a) 143 copies   **(b)** 217 copies

   (c) 310 copies   **(d)** 258 copies?

These comics also contain free gifts.

2  How many animal pencils are in

   (a) 143 copies   **(b)** 257 copies   **(c)** 179 copies?

3  How many pop pictures are in

   (a) 196 copies   **(b)** 180 copies   **(c)** 209 copies?

4  How many stickers are in

   (a) 207 copies   **(b)** 450 copies   **(c)** 386 copies?

5 This week *Soccer Scene* has 9 free football badges.
How many badges are in

   (a) 152 copies   **(b)** 263 copies   **(c)** 518 copies   **(d)** 768 copies?

6 This week's *MacTari* contains 10 free computer labels.
How many labels are in

   (a) 183 copies   **(b)** 497 copies   **(c)** 560 copies   **(d)** 900 copies?

SPEEDPRINT

1 Find the number of sheets

- in colour
- in black and white

in these copies of *Upbeat:*
(a) 2120   **(b)** 1203   **(c)** 2214

We print 2 sheets in colour and 4 sheets in black and white in each copy of *Upbeat*.

2 Find the total number of sheets in colour and in black and white in each of these magazines.

		Scream	Puzzles	Champs	Monster	Soaps
Number of copies		1106	2169	1078	1197	1168
Number of sheets	in colour	5	4	3	2	3
	in black and white	3	3	5	5	5

3 Which has more sheets **in colour**:

1033 copies of *Puzzles*   **or**   1295 copies of *Champs*?

After the magazines are printed we send them to warehouses.

4 A batch of 1265 copies of *Galaxy* is sent to each of 6 warehouses. How many copies are sent altogether?

5 Find the total number of copies of these magazines sent to warehouses.

	Cool	Galaxy	Charts	Donna	Stars
Number of copies to each warehouse	1336	1259	1184	1246	1052
Number of warehouses	7	7	8	8	9

Subscriptions

Some readers make a single payment
called a **subscription**. The magazine is then
posted to them each month for a year.

1 Each month 1815 copies of *Cool* are posted.
How many copies are posted in **(a)** 3 months   **(b)** 5 months?

2 Find the number of each of these magazines posted.

	Scream	Puzzles	Champs	Monster	Soaps
Copies posted in 1 month	2417	1538	1345	1248	1096
Number of months	4	6	7	8	9

3 How much does Mr. Bull pay for these envelopes?

(a) 3250 at 3p each   **(b)** 2358 at 3p each
(c) 2476 at 4p each   **(d)** 1853 at 4p each
(e) 1629 at 5p each   **(f)** 1387 at 5p each
(g) 1598 at 6p each   **(h)** 1476 at 6p each
(i) 1378 at 7p each   **(j)** 1259 at 7p each
(k) 1249 at 8p each   **(l)** 1187 at 8p each
(m) 1108 at 9p each   **(n)** 1079 at 9p each

Subscription to *Scream* £13.50

4 Seven people pay subscriptions to *Scream*. Find the total cost.

5 Find the total cost of these subscriptions for each magazine.

	Cool	Galaxy	Charts	Donna	Stars
Cost of 1 subscription	£15·75	£14·92	£13·69	£12·47	£10·36
Number of people	4	6	7	8	9

School Scene competition

**School Scene competition
Cross-number puzzle**

Autumn – 177 entries	Winter – 213 entries
Spring – 58 entries	Summer – 34 entries

1 Round each number of entries **to the nearest ten**.

2 Round **to the nearest ten**.

(a) 81   (b) 77   (c) 343   (d) 339   (e) 26   (f) 692

(g) 425   (h) 35   (i) 855   (j) 796   (k) 502   (l) 995

Steve

In Winter there were about 210 entries.
In Spring there were about 60 entries.
210 + 60 = 270, so altogether there
were **about** 270 entries.

3 **About** how many entries altogether were there in

(a) Spring and Summer?   (b) Winter and Summer?

4 Use Steve's method to find:

(a) 37 + 48   (b) 59 + 23   (c) 62 + 17   (d) 21 + 52   (e) 241 + 32

(f) 127 + 44   (g) 69 + 318   (h) 83 + 111   (i) 226 + 53   (j) 59 + 326

(k) 402 + 77   (l) 108 + 91   (m) 235 + 59   (n) 83 + 215   (o) 95 + 102

In Autumn there were about 180 entries.
In Spring there were about 60 entries.
180 − 60 = 120, so there were
about 120 more entries in Autumn.

Emma

5 **About** how many more entries were there in

(a) Spring than Summer?   (b) Autumn than Summer?

6 Use Emma's method to find:

(a) 83 − 41   (b) 88 − 46   (c) 59 − 32   (d) 73 − 24   (e) 87 − 18

(f) 161 − 33   (g) 186 − 54   (h) 248 − 27   (i) 152 − 41   (j) 279 − 53

(k) 386 − 78   (l) 134 − 28   (m) 265 − 29   (n) 192 − 55   (o) 475 − 67

Carnival café

1 The Carnival café can seat 464 people, four to a table. How many tables are there?

2 In the café car park there are 255 cars in 5 equal rows. How many cars are there in each row?

3 Five waiters serve 160 customers. How many customers should each waiter serve?

4 Carnival biscuits are sold in bags of three. How many bags are needed for

    (a) 162 biscuits   **(b)** 540 biscuits   **(c)** 876 biscuits?

5 Cakes are served four to a plate. How many plates are needed for 576 cakes?

6 Three freezers contain equal numbers of ice-cream tubs. How many tubs are in each freezer if altogether there are

    (a) 279 tubs   **(b)** 135 tubs   **(c)** 618 tubs?

7 **(a)** $2\overline{)559}$ **(b)** $3\overline{)710}$ **(c)** $4\overline{)305}$ **(d)** $5\overline{)809}$

    (e) $\frac{1}{2}$ of 754   **(f)** $\frac{1}{4}$ of 232   **(g)** $667 \div 5$ **(h)** $181 \div 2$

8

~Win a free meal!~

Find the winning number. It has

- a remainder of 1 when divided by 2
- a remainder of 2 when divided by 3
- a remainder of 3 when divided by 4.

Ticket 425 — free meal!
Ticket 895 — free meal!
Ticket 911 — free meal!
Ticket 784 — free meal!

Dragons

1 Share equally among 6 dragons:

    (a) 48 sticks   **(b)** 59 hoops   **(c)** 43 wheels

    (d) 78 egg boxes   **(e)** 92 pins   **(f)** 75 glue sticks

    (g) 366 spikes   **(h)** 522 paper sheets   **(i)** 717 feathers

2 Divide equally among 7 dragons:

    (a) 63 patches   **(b)** 51 tins of paint   **(c)** 29 balls of string

    (d) 85 ribbons   **(e)** 96 buttons   **(f)** 88 garlands

    (g) 217 corks   **(h)** 681 bells   **(i)** 579 flowers

3 **(a)** The total length of 6 identical dragons is 138 m.
        What is the length of one dragon?

    (b) Altogether the 6 dragons weigh 324 kg.
        What is the weight of one dragon?

4 **(a)** $140 \div 6$ **(b)** $192 \div 7$ **(c)** $99 \div 6$ **(d)** $100 \div 7$

    (e) $532 \div 6$ **(f)** $428 \div 7$ **(g)** $709 \div 7$ **(h)** $200 \div 6$

    (i) $6\overline{)603}$ **(j)** $7\overline{)930}$ **(k)** $6\overline{)655}$ **(l)** $7\overline{)882}$

5 How many boxes for   **(a)** 352 mugs   **(b)** 800 flags

                             (c) 206 pencils   **(d)** 142 ties?

Street decorations

1 Divide these decorations equally among 8 trees.

   (a) 72 red flags   **(b)** 63 blue flags   **(c)** 41 green flags

   (d) 93 streamers   **(e)** 109 hoops   **(f)** 231 stars

   (g) 652 triangles   **(h)** 523 balls   **(i)** 922 bits of tinsel

2 Share these fireworks equally for 9 displays.

   (a) 63 bangers   **(b)** 26 cascades   **(c)** 79 starbursts

   (d) 98 thunderflashes **(e)** 288 whizzies   **(f)** 951 sparklers

3 Paula shares paper flowers equally among 9 window boxes.
How many of each kind are in one window box?

   (a) 123 roses   **(b)** 221 irises   **(c)** 447 lilies

4 Paula puts 8 plants in each hanging basket.

   (a) How many baskets can she make with 362 plants?

   (b) How many plants are left over?

5 **(a)** $254 \div 8$ **(b)** $301 \div 9$ **(c)** $817 \div 8$ **(d)** $300 \div 9$

   (e) $899 \div 8$ **(f)** $980 \div 9$ **(g)** $600 \div 9$ **(h)** $511 \div 8$

   (i) $8\overline{)502}$ **(j)** $9\overline{)982}$ **(k)** $8\overline{)990}$ **(l)** $9\overline{)301}$

6 How many windows like this can be decorated with 450 lights?

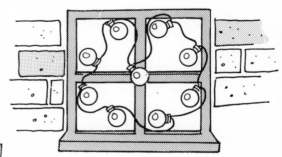

7 Each letter of this sign is lit by one spotlight.

How many CARNIVAL signs could be lit using 208 spotlights?

Carnival events

1 There are 10 floats in the procession.

(a) Share these equally among the 10 floats:

• 64 jesters   • 134 jugglers   • 258 dancers

(b) How many of each are left over?

(c) An equal number of children follow each float.
There are 420 children altogether.
How many are behind each float?

2 How many pyramids like this can be made from

(a) 74 acrobats   (b) 102 acrobats

(c) 230 acrobats   (d) 96 acrobats?

3 (a) 64 ÷ 2   (b) 114 ÷ 3   (c) 652 ÷ 5   (d) 814 ÷ 7

(e) 529 ÷ 4   (f) 176 ÷ 9   (g) 823 ÷ 2   (h) 717 ÷ 3

(i) 6)208   (j) 7)801   (k) 8)227   (l) 9)962

4 At the carnival, children dance in sets of 8.
How many sets can be made with

(a) 94 children   (b) 210 children   (c) 301 children?

5 438 children entered each of the competitions.

(a) How many teams of
• four were there for the relay races?
• six were there for the rowing?
• five were there for the football tournament?
• eight were there for the tug-of-war?

(b) In which competition did **all** the children take part?

(c) In which competition were most children left out?

Carnival fireworks

329 crackers in 7 boxes	695 starbursts in 5 boxes	846 rockets in 9 boxes	720 whizzos in 8 boxes

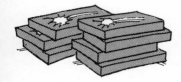   

1 Find the number of fireworks in each box.

2 Sparklers are sold in packs of 10.
How many packs are needed for 1350 sparklers?

3 How many tickets were sold for each stand at
the Fireworks Display?

Fireworks Display

	Stand	Cost of one ticket	Money from ticket sales
(a)	East	£6	£1428
(b)	West	£5	£ 995
(c)	South	£4	£1184
(d)	North	£7	£1652

4 Find the winning ticket.
The number on the winning ticket
divides exactly by 3, 4, 5, 6, 8
and 10.

1340	2120	1260

Prize draw

4940	9750	6720	4000

5 Food is sold at the Fireworks Display.

For every vegeburger sold, 10 pence
is given to charity.

If £36·90 was given to charity, how many vegeburgers were sold?

Carnival flags

Fractions: $\frac{1}{6}$, $\frac{1}{7}$, $\frac{1}{8}$, $\frac{1}{9}$; link with division

Heinemann Mathematics 5
Textbook page 45

17

1 For each flag, write the fraction • shaded • not shaded.

(a) 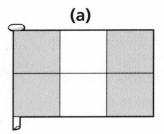 (b) 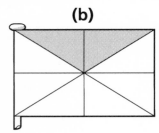 (c) 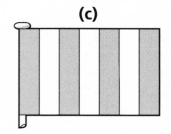 (d)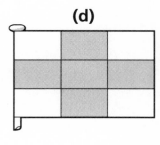

2 Draw the line of flags with the fractions **in order**.
Start with the **smallest** fraction.

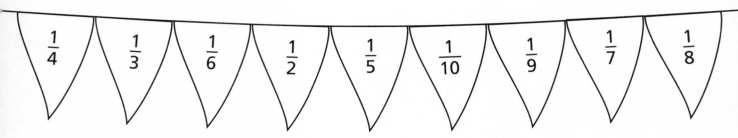

3 One eighth of the circles on each flag are to be black.
How many black circles should be on each flag?

(a) 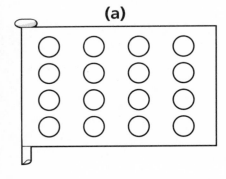 (b) 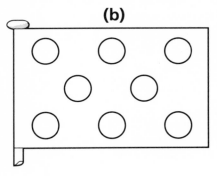 (c)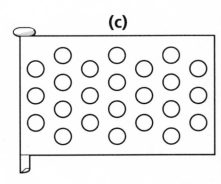

4 In the street there is a line of 49 carnival flags.
One seventh of them are coloured red.
How many flags are (a) red   (b) not red?

5 Find: (a) $\frac{1}{6}$ of 60   (b) $\frac{1}{7}$ of 21   (c) $\frac{1}{8}$ of 40
   (d) $\frac{1}{9}$ of 27   (e) $\frac{1}{8}$ of 64   (f) $\frac{1}{7}$ of 35
   (g) $\frac{1}{6}$ of 36   (h) $\frac{1}{7}$ of 63   (i) $\frac{1}{9}$ of 81
   (j) $\frac{1}{8}$ of 56   (k) $\frac{1}{9}$ of 90   (l) $\frac{1}{7}$ of 42

6 There 56 flags on a carnival display.
$\frac{1}{8}$ are green, $\frac{1}{7}$ are red and the rest are blue.

How many are (a) green   (b) red   (c) blue?

More carnival flags

1 Colour **one half** of each of these carnival flags.

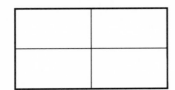

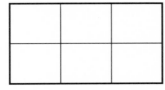

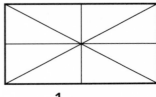

Complete: $\dfrac{1}{2} = \dfrac{}{4}$

$\dfrac{1}{2} = \dfrac{}{6}$

$\dfrac{1}{2} = \dfrac{}{8}$

2

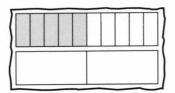

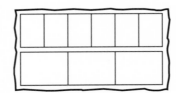

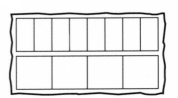

Colour
to show: $\dfrac{5}{10} = \dfrac{1}{2}$

$\dfrac{2}{6} = \dfrac{}{3}$

$\dfrac{2}{8} = \dfrac{}{4}$

Use these drawings to help you do questions 3 and 4.

1 whole			
$\frac{1}{2}$		$\frac{1}{2}$	
$\frac{1}{4}$	$\frac{1}{4}$	$\frac{1}{4}$	$\frac{1}{4}$
$\frac{1}{8}$ $\frac{1}{8}$	$\frac{1}{8}$ $\frac{1}{8}$	$\frac{1}{8}$ $\frac{1}{8}$	$\frac{1}{8}$ $\frac{1}{8}$

1 whole				
$\frac{1}{2}$			$\frac{1}{2}$	
$\frac{1}{5}$	$\frac{1}{5}$	$\frac{1}{5}$	$\frac{1}{5}$	$\frac{1}{5}$
$\frac{1}{10}$ $\frac{1}{10}$	$\frac{1}{10}$ $\frac{1}{10}$	$\frac{1}{10}$ $\frac{1}{10}$	$\frac{1}{10}$ $\frac{1}{10}$	$\frac{1}{10}$ $\frac{1}{10}$

3 Cross out the pairs of fractions which are **not equal**.

$\dfrac{1}{2} = \dfrac{3}{4}$

$\dfrac{1}{5} = \dfrac{3}{10}$

$\dfrac{2}{8} = \dfrac{2}{4}$

$\dfrac{3}{5} = \dfrac{6}{10}$

$\dfrac{10}{10} = \dfrac{5}{5}$

$\dfrac{3}{4} = \dfrac{7}{8}$

$\dfrac{2}{5} = \dfrac{1}{2}$

$\dfrac{2}{4} = \dfrac{4}{8}$

$\dfrac{4}{5} = \dfrac{8}{10}$

$\dfrac{2}{2} = \dfrac{8}{8}$

4 Complete:

$\dfrac{2}{10} = \dfrac{}{5}$

$\dfrac{5}{5} = \dfrac{10}{}$

$\dfrac{2}{8} = \dfrac{}{4}$

$\dfrac{3}{4} = \dfrac{6}{}$

$\dfrac{6}{10} = \dfrac{}{}$

Pennant parade

1 Write the decimal fraction of each design which is
  • shaded   • unshaded.

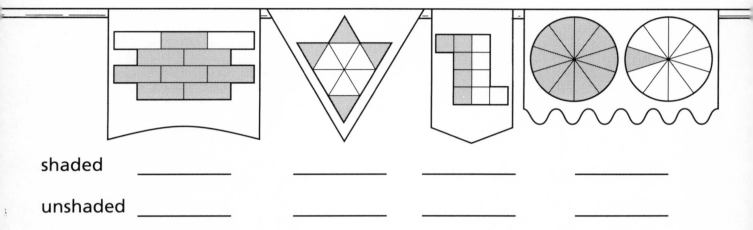

shaded   _____   _____   _____   _____

unshaded   _____   _____   _____   _____

2 Colour each design to show the decimal fraction.

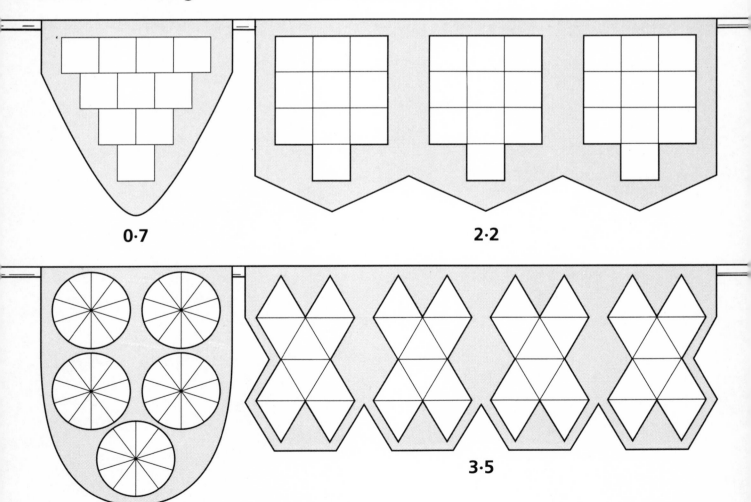

0·7   2·2

4·9   3·5

Hot air

1 There were **3·8** units of fuel in the balloon's tank at the start of the day. Write, in decimal form, the amount of fuel at the other times shown.

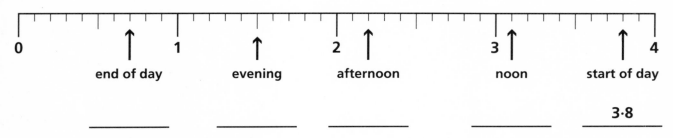

end of day	evening	afternoon	noon	start of day
				3·8
_____	_____	_____	_____	_____

2 Draw arrows on this gauge to show:

0·4   16 tenths   2·9   3 units and 3 tenths   37 tenths

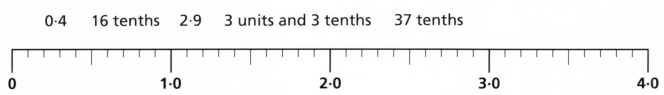

3 Complete the table to show the amount of fuel used in three different ways.

Sun	36 tenths	3 units and 6 tenths	3·6
Mon	25 tenths		
Tue		4 units and 4 tenths	
Wed			5·1
Thu	30 tenths		
Fri	9 tenths		
Sat			6·0

4 These displays show the balloon's height in metres at different times.

78·1	17·4	30·8	4·3	22·2

Circle a digit which has the value:

(a) 2 tenths   **(b)** 3 tenths   **(c)** 4 units   **(d)** 8 tenths   **(e)** 1 ten

Boat lengths

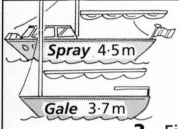

$$\begin{array}{r} 3.7\,m \\ +\,4.5\,m \\ \hline 8.2\,m \\ \end{array}$$
1

The total length of the two boats is **8·2 metres.**

1 Add these lengths.

(a)
$$\begin{array}{r} 3.8\,m \\ +\,3.9\,m \\ \hline \end{array}$$
(b)
$$\begin{array}{r} 2.4\,m \\ +\,4.6\,m \\ \hline \end{array}$$
(c)
$$\begin{array}{r} 4.7\,m \\ +\,2.6\,m \\ \hline \end{array}$$
(d)
$$\begin{array}{r} 3.8\,m \\ +\,4.0\,m \\ \hline \end{array}$$
(e)
$$\begin{array}{r} 5.5\,m \\ +\,5.5\,m \\ \hline \end{array}$$

(f) 3·6 m + 2·5 m   (g) 2·7 m + 4·4 m + 5 m   (h) 4·3 m + 3·9 m + 2·8 m

---

Spray 4·5 m

Gale 3·7 m

Spray is **0·8 metres** longer than *Gale*.

$$\begin{array}{r} \overset{3}{4}\overset{1}{.}5\,m \\ -\,3.7\,m \\ \hline 0.8\,m \\ \end{array}$$

2 Find the difference between these lengths.

(a)
$$\begin{array}{r} 5.3\,m \\ -\,2.9\,m \\ \hline \end{array}$$
(b)
$$\begin{array}{r} 3.0\,m \\ -\,2.7\,m \\ \hline \end{array}$$
(c)
$$\begin{array}{r} 4.1\,m \\ -\,2.0\,m \\ \hline \end{array}$$
(d)
$$\begin{array}{r} 3.5\,m \\ -\,2.6\,m \\ \hline \end{array}$$
(e)
$$\begin{array}{r} 4.8\,m \\ -\,3.9\,m \\ \hline \end{array}$$

(f) 3·6 m and 5 m   (g) 4·2 m and 2·5 m   (h) 3·4 m and 4·3 m

---

Lady of Lewis ← 21·7 m →

Lord of Lewis ← 25·4 m →

3 What is the total length of these two boats?

4 How much longer is the *Lord of Lewis* than than *Lady of Lewis*?

5 Add these lengths.

(a)
$$\begin{array}{r} 22.3\,m \\ +\,15.8\,m \\ \hline \end{array}$$
(b)
$$\begin{array}{r} 31.4\,m \\ +\,25.9\,m \\ \hline \end{array}$$
(c)
$$\begin{array}{r} 26.7\,m \\ +\,28.8\,m \\ \hline \end{array}$$
(d) 30·9 m and 9·1 m

(e) 7 m and 33·6 m

6 Find the difference between these lengths.

(a)
$$\begin{array}{r} 28.5\,m \\ -\,16.7\,m \\ \hline \end{array}$$
(b)
$$\begin{array}{r} 22.2\,m \\ -\,12.2\,m \\ \hline \end{array}$$
(c)
$$\begin{array}{r} 27.0\,m \\ -\,19.6\,m \\ \hline \end{array}$$
(d) 30·1 m and 29·9 m

(e) 28·4 m and 30 m

Keep Dry Clothing

Keep Dry Clothing make life jackets. Each label shows the jacket size and the length of material used to make it.

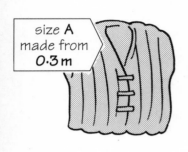
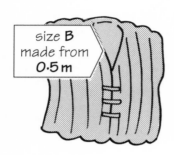
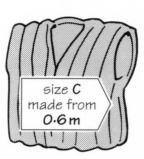

size A made from 0·3 m

size B made from 0·5 m

size C made from 0·6 m

size D made from 1·1 m

1 For each size A, B, C and D, calculate **mentally** the length of material used to make 10 lifejackets.

2 For each size A, B, C and D, calculate the length of material used to make
(a) 2 jackets   (b) 4 jackets   (c) 6 jackets   (d) 9 jackets.

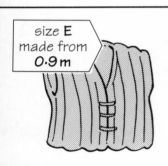
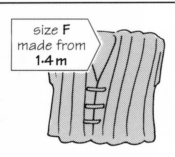

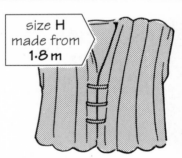

size E made from 0·9 m

size F made from 1·4 m

size G made from 1·7 m

size H made from 1·8 m

3 For each size, E to H, calculate the length of material used to make
(a) 5 jackets   (b) 7 jackets.

4 What length of material is used to make each of these orders:

(a) 3 cagoules
(b) 5 pairs of trousers
(c) 8 hooded jackets
(d) 4 sets of cagoules **and** trousers
(e) 9 sets of hooded jackets **and** trousers.

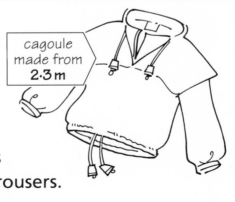

cagoule made from 2·3 m

hooded jacket made from 2·8 m

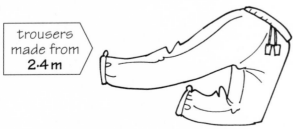

trousers made from 2·4 m

Orders

1 Each box shows the number of items and the **total** length of material used. Find the length used to make **one** item.

(a)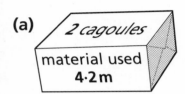

2 cagoules
material used
4·2 m

(b)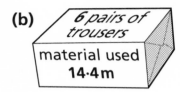

6 pairs of trousers
material used
14·4 m

(c)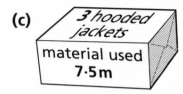

3 hooded jackets
material used
7·5 m

(d)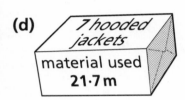

7 hooded jackets
material used
21·7 m

(e)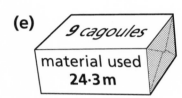

9 cagoules
material used
24·3 m

(f)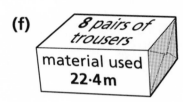

8 pairs of trousers
material used
22·4 m

2 What length of material is used to make **one** of the items in each of these orders:

(a)
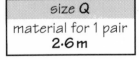
Order for Canoe Club
10 fitted jackets
made using 27 metres

(b)
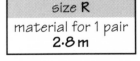
Order for Lewis Water Shop
10 raincoats
made using 34 metres

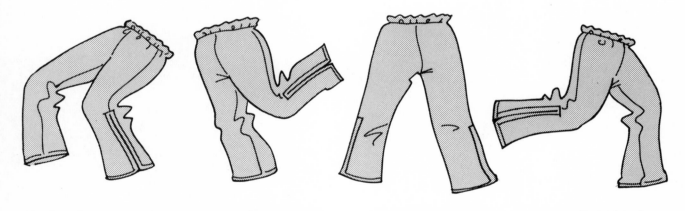

size P	size Q	size R	size S
material for 1 pair	material for 1 pair	material for 1 pair	material for 1 pair
2·4 m	**2·6 m**	**2·8 m**	**3·1 m**

3 Which trouser size is being ordered?

(a) Order for 2 pairs, made using 6·2 m of material altogether

(b) Order for 7 pairs, made using 18·2 m of material altogether

(c) Order for 6 pairs, made using 16·8 m of material altogether

(d) Order for 9 pairs, made using 21·6 m of material altogether

Sailing club

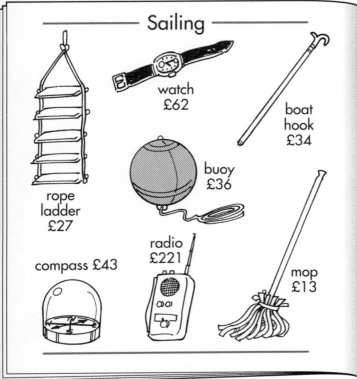

Sailing

rope ladder £27

watch £62

boat hook £34

buoy £36

compass £43

radio £221

mop £13

Catalogue

deck shoes £24

shorts £17

life jacket £46

gloves £19

cap £9

anorak £70

jumper £35

The captain finds the cost of 13 jumpers like this:	£35 × 3 ———— £105	£35 × 10 ———— £350	£105 + £350 ———— £455

1 Find the cost of these items:

(a) 11 mops
(b) 12 boat hooks
(c) 19 buoys
(d) 14 rope ladders
(e) 17 life jackets
(f) 15 watches
(g) 18 jumpers
(h) 16 pairs of deck shoes
(i) 13 pairs of shorts
(j) 19 compasses

2 Find the cost of 10 of each of these:

(a) caps
(b) mops
(c) boat hooks
(d) jumpers

3 Find the cost of 20 of each of these:

(a) rope ladders
(b) pairs of shorts
(c) buoys
(d) anoraks

4 Find the cost of:

(a) 30 life jackets
(b) 40 pairs of deck shoes
(c) 50 watches
(d) 30 compasses
(e) 60 pairs of gloves
(f) 80 boathooks

Training

Gordon swam under water for **493 centimetres**. That's **4 metres and 93 centimetres.**

1 Write each of these distances swum under water in another way.

	Jan	Naomi	Kris	Marie	Rashmi
1st swim	324 cm	419 cm	5 m 6 cm	3 m 40 cm	5 m 9 cm
2nd swim	3 m 55 cm	3 m 42 cm	4 m 85 cm	380 cm	395 cm

2 Calculate the **total** of the **two** distances for each swimmer.

In one stroke I can cover 3 m 56 cm. Last year I could only cover 2 m 90 cm.

Marie

$$\begin{array}{r} 356\,\text{cm} \\ -\ 290\,\text{cm} \\ \hline 66\,\text{cm} \end{array}$$

The difference for Marie is **66 cm**.

3 (a) Find the difference for each swimmer.

	Jan	Naomi	Kris	Gordon	Rashmi
This year	3 m 92 cm	3 m 15 cm	475 cm	5 m 6 cm	5 m
Last year	300 cm	3 m 11 cm	4 m 31 cm	395 cm	380 cm

(b) Which swimmer's distance increased • most • least?

Lotions and potions

1 Read the scale to find the weight of each ingredient.

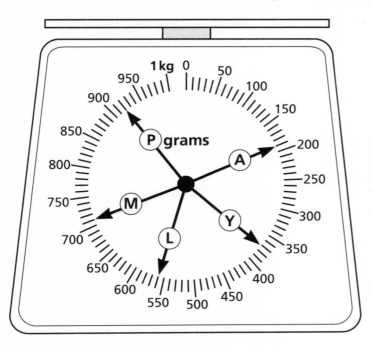

Zantha's Soothing Lotion

- (A) Apple
- (L) Lime
- (M) Marigolds
- (P) Parsley
- (Y) Yarrow

Simmer in violet
water for 15 minutes.

2 Zantha also makes **Potent Potion**.
Read the scales to find the
weight of each ingredient.

- (T) Thyme   (B) Basil
- (N) Nettles   (M) Mustard
- (L) Lavender (F) Fennel
- (S) Sage

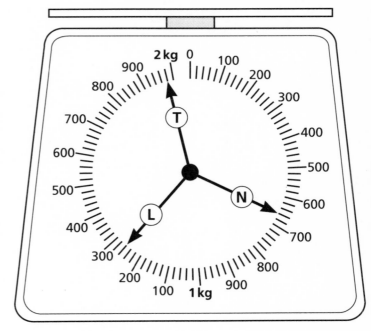

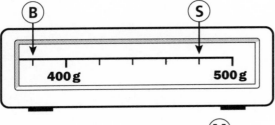

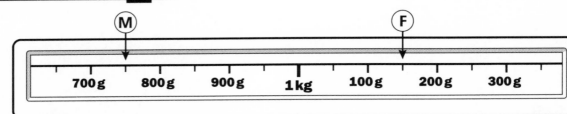

Name	Weight: scales	
	Heinemann Mathematics 5 Workbook page 29	

Kluless Cleaner

1 On the scales, draw pointers to show the weight of each ingredient used to make Kluless Cleaner.

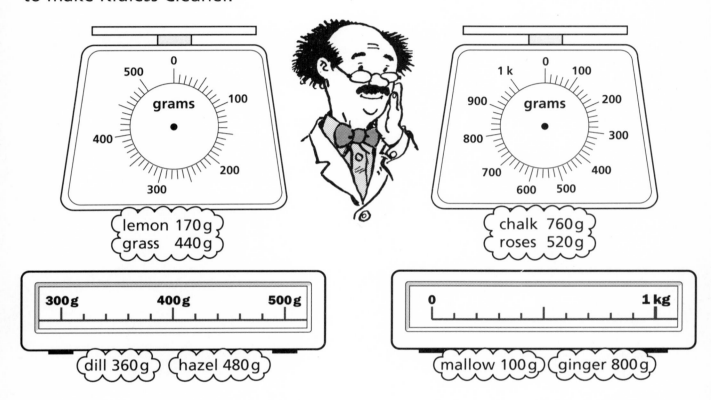

lemon 170g
grass 440g

chalk 760g
roses 520g

dill 360g   hazel 480g

mallow 100g   ginger 800g

2 For each of these ingredients:
• choose one of the scales
• draw a pointer to show its weight

haws 850g

hips 190g   hops 620g

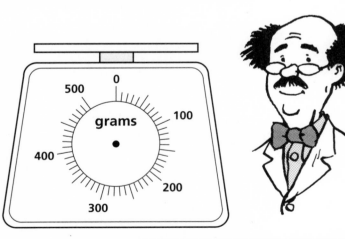

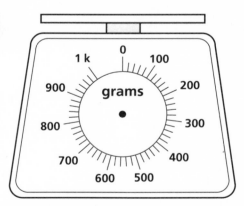

Sports day

1 The children made a video of the local sports day.
How many minutes of film did they take for each
of these events?

(a) sack race

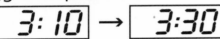
start → *finish*
`1:00` → `1:15`

(b) long jump

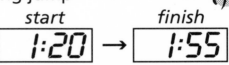
start → *finish*
`1:20` → `1:55`

(c) beat the keeper

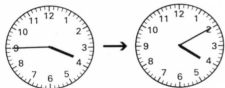
`2:05` → `2:25`

(d) high jump

`2:30` → `2:55`

(e) egg and spoon race

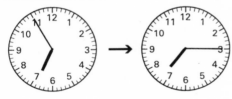
`3:10` → `3:30`

(f) obstacle race

`4:00` → `4:45`

(g) fun run

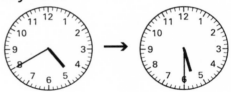

(h) relay race

(i) netball shoot

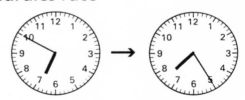

(j) hurdles race

2 For how long did each child watch the sports?
 (a) Karim: from 1.00 pm to 2.30 pm
 (b) Glen: from 1.15 pm to 2.20 pm
 (c) Roz: from 3.10 pm to 4.25 pm
 (d) Matt: from 5.00 pm to 6.20 pm

3 Six different teams took part
in the Sports Day.

How long did each team
take to travel home?

		leave sports	arrive home
(a)	Jets	7.00 pm	8.15 pm
(b)	Antelopes	7.20 pm	8.30 pm
(c)	Rockets	7.15 pm	7.55 pm
(d)	Fliers	7.30 pm	8.35 pm
(e)	Swifts	7.05 pm	8.00 pm
(f)	Whirlwinds	7.10 pm	8.25 pm

 Laser World

The children visit Laser World and take part in some of the adventures.

1 Find the finishing times.

	start at	play for
(a) Dragon Land	4.00pm	2 hours
(b) Dinosaur Valley	2.15pm	3 hours
(c) Giant Sponge	11.00am	1 hour

	start at	play for
(d) Planet X	9.30am	3 hours
(e) Central Core	6.50pm	1 hour
(f) Jittery Jungle	11.10am	2 hours

2 Find the finishing time for each child for each game.

	(a) Tessa starts at	plays for	(b) Roz starts at	plays for
Jittery Jungle	10.45am	40 minutes	9.40am	25 minutes
Dinosaur Valley	11.30am	50 minutes	10.35am	55 minutes
Central Core	12.50pm	35 minutes	11.55am	45 minutes

3 Each child plays the game 'Ocean Depths'.
Find the starting time for each player.

		plays for	finishes at
(a)	Tessa	2 hours	11.00am
(b)	Matt	2 hours	3.20pm
(c)	Mandy	1 hour	10.35am
(d)	Roz	2 hours	1.15pm

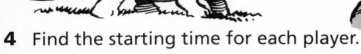

4 Find the starting time for each player.
   (a) Mandy found a dinosaur at noon, after 45 minutes.
   (b) Tessa met the giant sponge at 1.05pm, after 20 minutes.
   (c) Matt found the dragon at 11.10am, after 25 minutes.
   (d) Roz found the Central Core at 4.25pm, after 40 minutes.
   (e) Glen found a jitterbug at 3.35pm, after 50 minutes.

Sandra's yacht

1 Sandra is on the yacht. What does she see when she looks

  (a) West   _____

  (b) Northeast   _____

  (c) Northwest   _____

  (d) Southeast?   _____

2 In which direction is she facing when she turns from **North**

  (a) 90° clockwise   _____

  (b) 45° anti-clockwise   _____

  (c) 135° anti-clockwise   _____

  (d) 180° clockwise?   _____

3 Describe each of these turns which Sandra makes:

  (a) from North to Southeast   _____135° clockwise_____

  (b) from Northwest to Southwest   _____

  (c) from the wreck to the oil rig   _____

  (d) from the tanker to the marina   _____

4 Complete the table.

Sandra faces	she turns through	she now faces
marina	90° clockwise	
oil rig	45° anti-clockwise	
wreck		sand bank
	135° anti-clockwise	oil rig

Answers

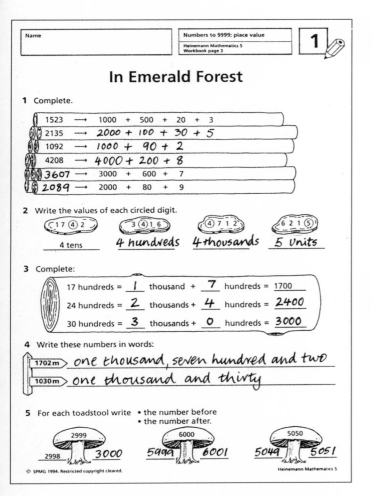

In Emerald Forest

1 Complete.

1523	→	1000 + 500 + 20 + 3
2135	→	2000 + 100 + 30 + 5
1092	→	1000 + 90 + 2
4208	→	4000 + 200 + 8
3607	→	3000 + 600 + 7
2089	→	2000 + 80 + 9

2 Write the values of each circled digit.

17④2 — 4 tens   3④16 — 4 hundreds   ④712 — 4 thousands   621⑤ — 5 units

3 Complete:

17 hundreds = **1** thousand + **7** hundreds = **1700**

24 hundreds = **2** thousands + **4** hundreds = **2400**

30 hundreds = **3** thousands + **0** hundreds = **3000**

4 Write these numbers in words:

1702m → one thousand, seven hundred and two

1030m → one thousand and thirty

5 For each toadstool write • the number before
• the number after.

2999 → 2998   3000

6000 → 5999   6001

5050 → 5049   5051

© SPMG 1994. Restricted copyright cleared.

Heinemann Mathematics 5

---

2   More tree puzzles

1
(a) 1800, 2000, 2200
(b) 1000, 900, 800
(c) 2090, 2100, 2110
(d) 1500, 1000, 500

2
(a) 2200   (b) 1206
(c) 2060   (d) 1008

3
(a) 4076, 4300, 4809, 5090, 5190
(b) 1001, 1100, 1101, 1110, 1111

4
(a) 3322
(b) 3232
(c) 2323

5
(a) 100   (b) 2000   (c) 40

6
(a) 50   (b) 3000   (c) 200

---

3   Trogball

1
(a) 6972   (b) 9724   (c) 9055
(d) 8022   (e) 8005   (f) 6303

2
(a) 7945
(b) 8212
(c) 6293
(d) 6037
(e) 6026
(f) 8201

3
(a) 5031   (b) 3001   (c) 3427   (d) 6228

---

4   Trog holiday survey

1
(a) 4313   (b) 4758
(c) 4983   (d) 5786

2 1028

3
(a) 777
(b) 704
(c) 1636

4
(a) 1889
(b) 3818
(c) 426
(d) 2315

---

5   Trogs in the swim

1
(a) 1998   (b) 668   (c) 3658

2
(a) 8900   (b) 8201
(c) 9543   (d) 8231

3
(a) 1438
(b) 829

4
(a) 4132
(b) 858
(c) 905

5 4533

6
(a) 9205
(b) 835

6 The four explorers

1 (a) £11·31
   (b) £12·98

2 £1·87

3 £2·14

4 (a) 10p + 20p + 50p + £1 + £1 + £1
   (b) 2p + 2p+ 20p + £1 + £5

5 £3·31

6 (a) Yes (Total cost £9·96)
   (b) No (Total cost £11·31)

7 £4·85 more

8 Yes. The total cost of bus fares,
   snack and pictures is £9·44

7 Comic collectors

1 **Andrew** 693   **Sarah** 910
   Humera 1228   **Asif** 472

2 (a) 572
   (b) 286
   (c) 429
   (d) 1144

3 (a) 774
   (b) 1503

4 (a) 870
   (b) 1743
   (c) 3500

8 Gifts

1 (a) 858   (b) 1302
   (c) 1860   (d) 1548

2 (a) 572   (b) 1028   (c) 716

3 (a) 1568   (b) 1440   (c) 1672

4 (a) 1449   (b) 3150   (c) 2702

5 (a) 1368   (b) 2367   (c) 4662   (d) 6912

6 (a) 1830   (b) 4970   (c) 5600   (d) 9000

9 Speedprint

1 (a) 4240 in colour, 8480 in black and white
   (b) 2406 in colour, 4812 in black and white
   (c) 4428 in colour, 8856 in black and white

2 *Scream* – 5530 in colour,
             3318 in black and white
   Puzzles – 8676 in colour,
             6507 in black and white
   Champs – 3234 in colour,
             5390 in black and white
   Monster – 2394 in colour,
             5985 in black and white
   Soaps – 3504 in colour,
             5840 in black and white

3 *Puzzles* has more pages in colour. It has 4132
   pages in colour. *Champs* has 3885 pages in
   colour.

4 7590 copies

5 *Cool* – 9352 copies
   Galaxy – 8813 copies
   Charts – 9472 copies
   Donna – 9968 copies
   Stars – 9468 copies

10 Subscriptions

1 (a) 5445 copies   (b) 9075 copies

2 *Scream* – 9668 copies
   Puzzles – 9228 copies
   Champs – 9415 copies
   Monster – 9984 copies
   Soaps – 9864 copies

3 (a) £97·50   (b) £70·74
   (c) £99·04   (d) £74·12
   (e) £81·45   (f) £69·35
   (g) £95·88   (h) £88·56
   (i) £96·46   (j) £88·13
   (k) £99·92   (l) £94·96
   (m)£99·72   (n) £97·11

4 £94·50

5 *Cool* – £63
   Galaxy – £89·52
   Charts – £95·83
   Donna – £99·76
   Stars – £93·24

11 *School Scene* competition

1 Autumn – 180 entries   Winter – 210 entries
Spring – 60 entries   Summer – 30 entries

2 (a) 80   (b) 80   (c) 340
(d) 340   (e) 30   (f) 690
(g) 420 or 430 (h) 30 or 40 (i) 850 or 860
(j) 800   (k) 500   (l) 990 or 1000

3 (a) about 90 entries
(b) about 240 or 250 entries

4 (a) about 90   (b) about 80   (c) about 80
(d) about 70   (e) about 270   (f) about 170
(g) about 390   (h) about 190   (i) about 280
(j) about 390   (k) about 480   (l) about 200
(m) about 290 or about 300
(n) about 290 or about 300
(o) about 190 or about 200

5 (a) about 30 more entries
(b) about 150 entries

6 (a) about 40   (b) about 40   (c) about 30
(d) about 50   (e) about 70   (f) about 130
(g) about 140   (h) about 220   (i) about 110
(j) about 230   (k) about 310   (l) about 100
(m) about 230 or about 240
(n) about 130 or about 140
(o) about 400 or about 410

12 Carnival café

1 116 tables

2 51 cars

3 32 customers

4 (a) 54 bags   (b) 180 bags   (c) 292 bags

5 144 plates

6 (a) 93 tubs   (b) 45 tubs   (c) 206 tubs

7 (a) 279 r 1 (b) 236 r 1 (c) 76 r 1 (d) 161 r 4
(e) 377   (f) 58   (g) 133 r 2 (h) 90 r 1

8 911 is the winning number

13 Dragons

1 (a) 8 sticks
(b) 9 hoops (and 5 left over)
(c) 7 wheels (and 1 left over)
(d) 13 egg boxes
(e) 15 pins (and 2 left over)
(f) 12 glue sticks (and 3 left over)
(g) 61 spikes
(h) 87 paper sheets
(i) 119 feathers (and 3 left over)

2 (a) 9 patches
(b) 7 tins of paint (and 2 left over)
(c) 4 balls of string (and 1 left over)
(d) 12 ribbons (and 1 left over)
(e) 13 buttons (and 5 left over)
(f) 12 garlands (and 4 left over)
(g) 31 corks
(h) 97 bells (and 2 left over)
(i) 82 flowers (and 5 left over)

3 (a) 23 metres   (b) 54 kilograms

4 (a) 23 r 2   (b) 27 r 3   (c) 16 r 3   (d) 14 r 2
(e) 88 r 4   (f) 61 r 1   (g) 101 r 2 (h) 33 r 2
(i) 100 r 3 (j) 132 r 6 (k) 109 r 1 (l) 126

5 (a) 59 boxes   (b) 115 boxes
(c) 30 boxes   (d) 24 boxes

14 Street decorations

1 (a) 9 red flags
(d) 7 blue flags (and 7 left over)
(c) 5 green flags (and 1 left over)
(d) 11 streamers (and 5 left over)
(e) 13 hoops (and 5 left over)
(f) 28 stars (and 7 left over)
(g) 81 triangles (and 4 left over)
(h) 65 balls (and 3 left over)
(i) 115 bits of tinsel (and 2 left over)

2 (a) 7 bangers
(b) 2 cascades (and 8 left over)
(c) 8 starbursts (and 7 left over)
(d) 10 thunderflashes (and 8 left over)
(e) 32 whizzies
(f) 105 sparklers (and 6 left over)

3 (a) 13 roses (and 6 left over)
(b) 24 irises (and 5 left over)
(c) 49 lilies (and 6 left over)

4 (a) 45 baskets
(b) 2 plants

14 Street decorations – continued

5 (a) 31 r 6 (b) 33 r 4 (c) 102 r 1 (d) 33 r 3
(e) 112 r 3 (f) 108 r 8 (g) 66 r 6 (h) 63 r 7
(i) 62 r 6 (j) 109 r 1 (k) 123 r 6 (l) 33 r 4

6 50 windows

7 26 signs

15 Carnival events

1 (a), (b)
- 6 jesters and 4 left over
- 13 jugglers and 4 left over
- 25 dancers and 8 left over

(c) 42 children

2 (a) 12 pyramids (and 2 acrobats left over)
(b) 17 pyramids
(c) 38 pyramids (and 2 acrobats left over)
(d) 16 pyramids

3 (a) 32 (b) 38 (c) 130 r 2 (d) 116 r 2
(e) 132 r 1 (f) 19 r 5 (g) 411 r 1 (h) 239
(i) 34 r 4 (j) 114 r 3 (k) 28 r 3 (l) 106 r 8

4 (a) 11 sets (and 6 children left over)
(b) 26 sets (and 2 children left over)
(c) 37 sets (and 5 children left over)

5 (a)
- 109 teams (and 2 left over)
- 73 teams
- 87 teams (and 3 left over)
- 54 teams (and 6 left over)

(b) All the children took part in the rowing.
(c) Most children were left out in the tug-of-war.

16 Carnival fireworks

1 47 crackers
139 starbursts
94 rockets
90 whizzos

2 135 packs

3 (a) 238 tickets
(b) 199 tickets
(c) 296 tickets
(d) 236 tickets

4 6720 is the winning ticket

5 369 vege-burgers

17 Carnival flags

1 (a) $\frac{4}{6}$ shaded $\frac{2}{6}$ unshaded
(b) $\frac{2}{8}$ shaded $\frac{6}{8}$ unshaded
(c) $\frac{4}{7}$ shaded $\frac{3}{7}$ unshaded
(d) $\frac{5}{9}$ shaded $\frac{4}{9}$ unshaded

2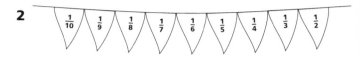

3 (a) 2 black circles (b) 1 black circle
(c) 3 black circles

4 (a) 7 flags are red (b) 42 flags are not red

5 (a) 10 (b) 3 (c) 5
(d) 3 (e) 8 (f) 5
(g) 6 (h) 9 (i) 9
(j) 7 (k) 10 (l) 6

6 (a) 7 flags are green (b) 8 flags are red
(c) 41 flags are blue

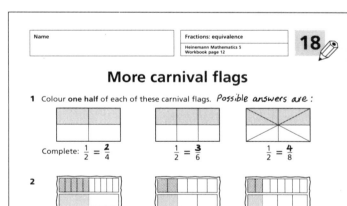

Name ___

Fractions: equivalence
Heinemann Mathematics 5
Workbook page 12

18

More carnival flags

1 Colour **one half** of each of these carnival flags. *Possible answers are :*

Complete: $\frac{1}{2} = \frac{2}{4}$ $\frac{1}{2} = \frac{3}{6}$ $\frac{1}{2} = \frac{4}{8}$

2
Colour to show: $\frac{5}{10} = \frac{1}{2}$ $\frac{2}{6} = \frac{1}{3}$ $\frac{2}{8} = \frac{1}{4}$

Use these drawings to help you do questions 3 and 4.

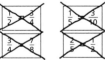

3 Cross out the pairs of fractions which are **not equal**.

   $\frac{2}{8} = \frac{2}{4}$ $\frac{3}{5} = \frac{6}{10}$ $\frac{10}{10} = \frac{5}{5}$

$\frac{3}{4} = \frac{7}{8}$ $\frac{2}{5} = \frac{1}{5}$ $\frac{2}{4} = \frac{4}{8}$ $\frac{4}{5} = \frac{8}{10}$ $\frac{2}{2} = \frac{8}{8}$

4 Complete:
  $\frac{5}{5} = \frac{10}{10}$ $\frac{2}{8} = \frac{1}{4}$ $\frac{3}{4} = \frac{6}{8}$ $\frac{6}{10} = \frac{3}{5}$

Pennant parade

1 Write the decimal fraction of each design which is
• shaded   • unshaded.

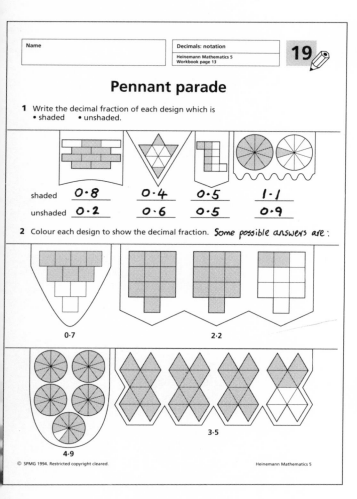

shaded	0·8	0·4	0·5	1·1
unshaded	0·2	0·6	0·5	0·9

2 Colour each design to show the decimal fraction. *Some possible answers are:*

0·7   2·2

3·5

4·9

© SPMG 1994. Restricted copyright cleared.   Heinemann Mathematics 5

Hot air

1 There were 3·8 units of fuel in the balloon's tank at the start of the day.
Write, in decimal form, the amount of fuel at the other times shown.

end of day	evening	afternoon	noon	start of day
0·7	1·5	2·2	3·1	3·8

2 Draw arrows on this gauge to show:

0·4   16 tenths   2·9   3 units and 3 tenths   37 tenths

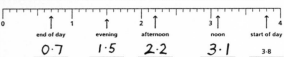

0·4   16 tenths   2·9   3 units and 3 tenths   37 tenths

3 Complete the table to show the amount of fuel used in three different ways.

Sun	36 tenths	3 units and 6 tenths	3·6
Mon	25 tenths	2 units and 5 tenths	2·5
Tue	44 tenths	4 units and 4 tenths	4·4
Wed	51 tenths	5 units and 1 tenth	5·1
Thu	30 tenths	3 units and 0 tenth	3·0
Fri	9 tenths	0 units and 9 tenths	0·9
Sat	60 tenths	Six units and 0 tenths	6·0

4 These displays show the balloon's height in metres at different times.

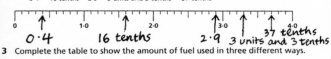

78·1   1⑦·4   30·⑧   ④③   22·②

Circle a digit which has the value:
(a) 2 tenths **(b)** 3 tenths **(c)** 4 units **(d)** 8 tenths **(e)** 1 ten

© SPMG 1994. Restricted copyright cleared.   Heinemann Mathematics 5

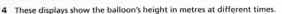

---

21   Boat lengths

1 **(a)** 7·7 m **(b)** 7·0 m **(c)** 7·3 m **(d)** 7·8 m
   (e) 11·0 m **(f)** 6·1 m **(g)** 12·1 m **(h)** 11·0 m

2 **(a)** 2·4 m **(b)** 0·3 m **(c)** 2·1 m **(d)** 0·9 m
   (e) 0·9 m **(f)** 1·4 m **(g)** 1·7 m **(h)** 0·9 m

3 The total length of the two boats is 47·1 m.

4 The *Lord of Lewis* is 3·7 m longer than the
   Lady of Lewis.

5 **(a)** 38·1 m **(b)** 57·3 m **(c)** 55·5 m
   (d) 40·0 m **(e)** 40·6 m

6 **(a)** 11·8 m **(b)** 10·0 m **(c)** 7·4 m
   (d) 0·2 m **(e)** 1·6 m

22   Keep Dry Clothing

1 A – 3 m   B – 5 m   C – 6 m   D – 11 m

2 **(a)** A – 0·6 m, B – 1·0 m, C – 1·2 m, D – 2·2 m
   (b) A – 1·2 m, B – 2·0 m, C – 2·4 m, D – 4·4 m
   (c) A – 1·8 m, B – 3·0 m, C – 3·6 m, D – 6·6 m
   (d) A – 2·7 m, B – 4·5 m, C – 5·4 m, D – 9·9 m

3 **(a)** E – 4·5 m, F – 7·0 m, G – 8·5 m, H – 9·0 m
   (b) A – 6·3 m, F – 9·8 m, G – 11·9 m, H – 12·6 m

4 **(a)** 6·9 m
   (b) 12·0 m
   (c) 22·4 m
   (d) 18·8 m
   (e) 28·8 m

23   Orders

1 **(a)** 2·1 m **(b)** 2·4 m **(c)** 2·5 m
   (d) 3·1 m **(e)** 2·7 m **(f)** 2·8 m

2 **(a)** 2·7 m **(b)** 3·4 m

3 **(a)** size S was ordered
   (b) size Q was ordered
   (c) size R was ordered
   (d) size P was ordered

24 Sailing club

1. (a) £143   (b) £408
   (c) £684   (d) £378
   (e) £782   (f) £930
   (g) £630   (h) £384
   (i) £221   (j) £817

2. (a) £90   (b) £130   (c) £340   (d) £350

3. (a) £540   (b) £340   (c) £720   (d) £1400

4. (a) £1380   (b) £960
   (c) £3100   (d) £1290
   (e) £1140   (d) £2720

26 Lotions and potions

1. A ⟶ 190 g
   Y ⟶ 370 g
   L ⟶ 560 g
   M ⟶ 710 g
   P ⟶ 920 g

2. T ⟶ 1 kg 980 g   B ⟶ 380 g
   N ⟶ 660 g   M ⟶ 750 g
   L ⟶ 1 kg 260 g   F ⟶ 1 kg 150 g
   S ⟶ 480 g

25 Training

1.

Jan	Naomi	Kris	Marie	Rashmi
3 m 24 cm	4 m 19 cm	506 cm	340 cm	509 cm
355 cm	342 cm	485 cm	3 m 80 cm	3 m 95 cm

2.   Jan — 6 m 79 cm
   Naomi — 7 m 61 cm
        Kris — 9 m 91 cm
      Marie — 7 m 20 cm
   Rashmi — 9 m 4 cm

3. (a)   Jan —   92 cm
       Naomi —   4 cm
         Kris —   44 cm
   Gordon — 1 m 11 cm
     Rashmi — 1 m 20 cm

   (b) Rashmi's distance increased most.
   Naomi's distance increased least.

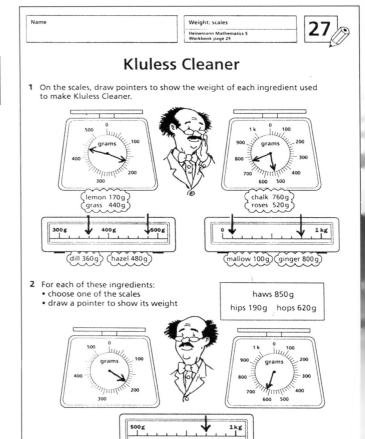

1 (a) 15 minutes (b) 35 minutes
(c) 20 minutes (d) 25 minutes
(e) 20 minutes (f) 45 minutes
(g) 25 minutes (h) 50 minutes
(i) 20 minutes (j) 35 minutes

2 (a) 1 hour 30 minutes
(b) 1 hour 5 minutes
(c) 1 hour 15 minutes
(d) 1 hour 20 minutes

3 (a) 1 hour 15 minutes
(b) 1 hour 10 minutes
(c) 1 hour 40 minutes
(d) 1 hour 5 minutes
(e) 55 minutes
(f) 1 hour 15 minutes

1 (a) 6.00 pm (d) 12.30 pm
(b) 5.15 pm (e) 7.50 pm
(c) 12.00 noon (f) 1.10 pm

2

	(a) Tessa	(b) Roz
Jittery Jungle	11.25 am	10.05 am
Dinosaur Valley	12.20 pm	11.30 am
Central Core	1.25 pm	12.40 pm

3 (a) 9.00 am
(b) 1.20 pm
(c) 9.35 am
(d) 11.15 am

4 (a) 11.15 am
(b) 12.45 pm
(c) 10.45 am
(d) 3.45 pm
(e) 2.45 pm

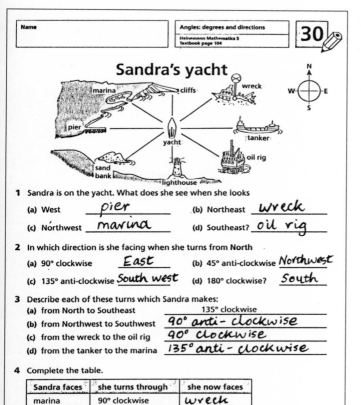

Name	Angles: degrees and directions	**30**
	Heinemann Mathematics 5 Textbook page 104	

Sandra's yacht

1 Sandra is on the yacht. What does she see when she looks

(a) West *pier*
(b) Northeast *wreck*
(c) Northwest *marina*
(d) Southeast? *oil rig*

2 In which direction is she facing when she turns from North

(a) 90° clockwise *East*
(b) 45° anti-clockwise *Northwest*
(c) 135° anti-clockwise *South west*
(d) 180° clockwise? *South*

3 Describe each of these turns which Sandra makes:
(a) from North to Southeast *135° clockwise*
(b) from Northwest to Southwest *90° anti-clockwise*
(c) from the wreck to the oil rig *90° clockwise*
(d) from the tanker to the marina *135° anti-clockwise*

4 Complete the table.

Sandra faces	she turns through	she now faces
marina	90° clockwise	*wreck*
oil rig	45° anti-clockwise	*tanker*
wreck	*180 anti-clockwise*	sand bank
pier	135° anti-clockwise	oil rig

© SPMG 1994. Restricted copyright cleared. ✳ *or clockwise*   Heinemann Mathematics 5